First Day of Second Grade

by Eric Mancilla
illustrated by Julie Downing

 HOUGHTON MIFFLIN   BOSTON

Printed in China

ISBN-13: 978-0-547-03006-7
ISBN-10: 0-547-03006-1

5 6 7 8 9 0940 15 14 13
4500396734

bus

Juan

Brooke

bus stop

It was the first day of school.
It was the first day of
second grade!
Juan was seven.
"I can go to the bus stop
by myself!" Juan said.

Brooke was at the bus stop, too.
Brooke was Juan's friend.
"Look! Here comes the bus,"
said Juan.
Juan and Brooke got on the bus.

Juan looked at Brooke.
She seemed sad.
"What's wrong?" said Juan.
"Will second grade be hard?
Will I like our teacher,
Ms. Willows?" said Brooke.

Jeff

"I can tell you all about
Ms. Willows!" said a boy
behind them.
"My name is Jeff."
"Oh, please tell me," said
Brooke.

"I like Ms. Willows a lot," said
Jeff. "She is nice."
Juan asked, "Will second grade
be hard?"
"Kids say it is hard," said Jeff.
"But Ms. Willows will help you."

"Did you like second grade
last year?" said Juan.
"I am in second grade this year!"
said Jeff.
"What?" said Brooke.

"I was in first grade last year,"
said Jeff. "My family lived
in a different city."
"How can you tell us about
Ms. Willows?" said Juan.
"Ms. Willows is my mom!"
said Jeff.

Ms. Willows

card

kids

Jeff said, "All the kids like my mom. The kids buy cards for my mom. The kids thank my mom for her help."

"Second grade can be hard, but my mom will help you. Second grade will be fun," said Jeff.

Brooke, Juan, and Jeff walked
into class.
Ms. Willows had a party for the
first day of school!
Brooke said, "We will like
second grade!"

Responding

Understanding Characters What is Brooke like? What does Brooke say? What does Brooke do? How does Brooke feel? Make a chart.

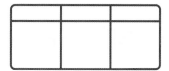

Talk About It

Text to Self Think about your first day of school. How did you feel at the beginning of the day? What did you do? How did you feel at the end of the day?

11

✔ WORDS TO KNOW

buy	party
city	please
family	school
myself	seven

✔ **TARGET SKILL** **Understanding Characters** Tell more about characters.

✔ **TARGET STRATEGY** **Summarize** Stop to tell important events as you read.

GENRE Realistic fiction is a story that could happen in real life.